BRAHMS

Three Intermezzos
Op. 117

Edited & annotated by

HOWARD FERGUSON

ABRSM

Published by ABRSM (Publishing) Ltd, a wholly owned subsidiary of ABRSM

CONTENTS

Three Intermezzos, Op. 117

INTRODUCTION

Johannes Brahms
(1833-1897)

The solo piano music of Brahms falls into three fairly distinct groups: (1) Three early, romantic Sonatas (C major, Op.1; F sharp minor, Op.2, which was actually the first; and F minor, Op.5), plus the isolated Scherzo in E flat minor, Op.4. (2) Five slightly later, self-disciplining sets of Variations. (3) Seven groups of shorter pieces that make up the present series of volumes, all being late except the *Four Ballads*, Op.10.

Besides these, pianists should not overlook the five splendid works for two players on one piano: *Variations on a theme by Schumann*, Op.23; 16 *Waltzes*, Op.39 (also published in two solo piano versions, simplified and difficult, made by Brahms himself); *Liebeslieder* and *Neue Liebeslieder Waltzes*, Op.52 & 65 (with four optional mixed voices); and 21 *Hungarian Dances*. And also, for two pianos, the *Sonata in F minor*, Op.34b, and *Variations on a theme by Haydn*, Op.56b, the composer's own versions of, respectively, the Piano Quintet in F minor and the well-known Haydn-Variations for orchestra.

SOURCES

Brahms took immense pains to secure accuracy in his published compositions. Furthermore, he kept a copy of the 1st edition of each work and noted in it any mistakes that had been overlooked at the proof stage. (Many works required no correction.) Hence it is these personally corrected copies rather than the autographs that provide the definitive texts of his music. He bequeathed them to the Gesellschaft der Musikfreunde in Vienna; and it is thanks to that Society that it has been possible to use them for the preparation of the present edition.

TEMPO

Brahms' main tempo marks are generally clear and unambiguous. But he used the word *sostenuto* in a special sense, implying a perceptible drop in speed. For example, in the Ballad in G minor, Op.118/3, b.71, *poco sosten.* is followed by *poco a poco in tempo* several bars later. Sometimes *sostenuto sempre* refers to a longer self-contained passage, as in the Rhapsody in B minor, Op.79/1, b.22. Here it undoubtedly remains in force for at least eight bars, and most probably for seventeen, since the vigorous mood of the opening does not return until b.39, where *in tempo* follows a further 2-bar *poco rit.* The duration of a shorter *sostenuto* is generally shown by dashes (*sost.* – – –), with *a tempo* implied (though not indicated) where the dashes cease, as in the Intermezzo in C, Op.119/3, b.10. But note that two

bars later the *sost.* applies to no more than a single quaver.

More rarely a similar drop in tempo is implied by the word *tranquillo*, as in the Capriccio in C sharp minor, Op.76/5, where *poco tranquillo* is shown at b.53, followed by *poco a poco più tranquillo* above bb.58-61, *rit.* – – – above bb.65-68, and finally *Tempo I* at b.69.

Brahms never used metronome marks. When asked for the correct marking for his Rhapsody in B minor, Op.79/1, he replied that he could not give one, as it would be different for every week. And on several occasions he tried (unavailingly) to dissuade Clara Schumann from adding her own metronome marks to the posthumous edition of her husband's complete works.

In spite of this, the present editor has had the temerity to include in his Notes a suggested metronome mark for each piece. It must be understood, however, that it has no authority whatever, and may be ignored if the player so wishes. Far more important is it to remember that Brahms' music generally requires space in which to 'breathe', and will rarely sound right if forced into the straightjacket of a mechanical beat.

FINGERING

Though Brahms only occasionally indicated his own fingering – in these volumes it is always shown in italics – the shape of some of his broken-chord passages shows that they must be fingered in an unusual way. Instead of passing the thumb under the 3rd or 4th finger, or the 3rd or 4th finger over the thumb, the broken-chord is divided into complete handfuls, and the pedal used to mask the break in legato that occurs when jumping from thumb to 5th finger or *vice versa*. For example, in the Capriccio in D minor, Op.116/7, bb.61-63 must be fingered thus:

otherwise the effect of both slurs and accents will be lost. And in the Rhapsody in E flat, Op.119/4, the l.h. passage at bb.39-40 is undoubtedly meant to be fingered:

Many of Brahms' keyboard textures suggest that he had an unusually wide hand-span. Players not similarly blessed should discreetly break chords they cannot stretch, either as quick arpeggios or with the lowest note played as a gracenote before the beat and sustained by pedal.

ARPEGGIOS

An arpeggio sign (⁞) in Brahms often implies a momentary broadening of tempo. In theory the arpeggio should begin on the beat, and it generally does so when in the r.h. alone. If in the l.h. alone it often begins before the beat, its top note coinciding with the beat itself. The overriding consideration, however, must always be to avoid a thin tonal effect; so the player should interpet each arpeggio in the way that seems best suited to its musical context.

PEDALLING

The paired signs, *Ped.*　✲ , indicate no more than the essential use of the sustaining pedal. Elsewhere, and often for a whole piece, Brahms expects the player to supply whatever pedalling may be required. Sometimes the general indication, *col Ped.* , appears at the beginning of a piece, as in the Intermezzo in B flat minor, Op.117/2; but it may or may not be followed by anything further. In the same Intermezzo *Ped.*　✲ does in fact appear twice in bb.8-9; yet it is interesting to note that the apparently similar passage at bb.21-22 is left unmarked, in spite of the fact that it needs different pedalling, with a change on beat 3 of the 1st bar (to match the shift in r.h. harmony) instead of on beat 1 of the 2nd bar, as bb.8-9 would suggest. In the Intermezzo in E flat, Op.117/1, the only two indications are *col Ped.* at the return of the opening (b.38), and *Ped.* in the penultimate bar; but this of course does not mean that there should be no pedal elsewhere.

Pedalled passages often contain rests and/or staccato marks (*e.g.* in Op.10/3, bb.3-6, and Op.10/2, b.91). Though illogical, this convention is acceptable because the presence of rests may simplify notation, while staccato marks suggest a type of touch or attack which, in conjunction with the pedal, produces a sound perceptibly different from that of a legato.

The sign for the 'soft' pedal, *una corda*, is rare; but it too may be supplemented by the player, so long as he doesn't get into the habit of adding it whenever he sees a *p*. Sometimes it is cancelled by the words *tre corde* or *tutte corde*, and sometimes the cancellation is left to the player's discretion, as in the Intermezzo in B flat already mentioned.

THIS EDITION

In the present edition numbered footnotes are concerned with textual matters and lettered footnotes with points of interpretation. Editorial accidentals, rests, dynamics, etc., are printed either in small type or within square brackets, and editorial slurs are crossed with a small vertical stroke. Curved brackets indicate that a note should not be struck. Brahms' fingering is shown in italics and the editor's in arabic numerals. Occasionally the editor has altered the distribution of notes on the stave, or employed the signs ⌈ and ⌊ (indicating respectively left hand and right hand), when this might make the text easier to read.

Warmest thanks are due to the Gesellschaft der Musikfreunde, Vienna, for providing microfilms of the 1st editions containing Brahms' corrections; to the Pendelbury Library, Cambridge, for allowing access to other 1st editions; and to both authorities for giving permission for the use of this material in preparing the present texts.

HOWARD FERGUSON
Cambridge 1985

EDITORIAL NOTES

The *Three Intermezzos* were composed in 1892 and were first published as *Drei Intermezzi,* Op.117; N. Simrock, Berlin 1892 [no Pl.No.].

1 INTERMEZZO IN E FLAT

Andante moderato [♪ = c.92];
Più Adagio [♪ = c.80]

The couplet quoted by Brahms comes from Gottfried Herder's translation of the anonymous Scottish poem known as 'Lady Anne Bothwell's Lament' (Thomas Percy, *Reliques of Ancient English Poetry,* 1765, Series II, Book 2, XIII). It is a lullaby sung by an unhappy mother whose lover has deserted herself and their child.

At the opening the melody in the r.h. middle part must stand out clearly and evenly from the surrounding chords. Care is needed where the two lie close together, and when the melody shifts from an inner to an outer part. On the final quaver of b.6 the l.h. assumes equal importance for two bars. In b.8 the r.h. arpeggio implies, as so often in Brahms, a slight broadening of the tempo, here lasting until the end of the bar.

The *poco a poco rit.* beginning at b.15 is simplified if there is a return to almost the original tempo for two bars from the last quaver of b.16, followed by an immediate resumption of the *rit.* As the pause at the end of b.20 is above the barline it means a silence, not a prolongation of the previous chord.

A surprising number of pianists play the *Più Adagio* quicker than the *Andante moderato.* This is a mistake, for not only does it contradict Brahms' marking, but it sentimentalizes the opening and misses the tragic mood of the middle section. Most of it should be pedalled in half-bars, in spite of the r.h. staccato marks and l.h. rests. But possibly not in b.31, and certainly not in bb.26, 28 & 34, where the recollection of the opening requires 'clean' pedalling and (like a parenthesis) a lower dynamic level than its surroundings. In b.36 bring out the augmentation of the 'recollection' in the lower l.h. line, followed by its echo a bar later in the octaves between the hands.

When the opening returns (b.38) make sure that the octave melody passes smoothly from hand to hand. Though there is no arpeggio in b.45, the phrase requires the same extra space that it was given at b.8. Entirely new is the expressive canon between the two upper voices in bb.50-51. It can begin somewhat hesitantly, then gently gather momentum as it proceeds. In the final two bars the pedal should not be released (again in spite of the rests) until after the pause in b.57.

2 INTERMEZZO IN B FLAT MINOR

Andante non troppo [♪ = c.72]; b.27, etc. [♪ = c.66];
Più Adagio [♪ = c.54];

Brahms sometimes based an apparently new subject on a transformation of material heard earlier, thus combining unity with diversity. In this Intermezzo, for example, the beginning of the 'new' theme that starts with the final three semiquavers of b.22 has exactly the same melodic outline as the opening two bars:

Though the resemblance between the two lessens, their general shape is recognizably similar in spite of differences of detail.

In bb.1-6, etc., three dynamic levels are required. In descending order of importance they are: 1) the r.h. melody, indicated by 2-note slurs (and small crosses in the above example); 2) the l.h. semiquavers; and 3) the remaining demisemiquavers, which, with the help of pedal-changes on the 1st & 3rd quavers of every bar, provide the textural background. In b.9 the harmony is altered by the 1st l.h. note, which (in spite of the *pp*) needs to be slightly stressed.

In b.21 the pedal-change (unmarked) is on the 3rd quaver, to match the harmonic shift in the r.h.

The *rit.* in bb.21-22 & 29-30 suggests that the *sostenuto* should begin with the 'new' theme, half way through bb.22 & 30 rather than several bars later. This would also allow some extra time for the r.h. arpeggios in bb.24-25 & 32-33. In any case, *Tempo I* returns in the middle of b.38.

A long *cresc.*, beginning in b.61, builds up to a powerful climax on beat 1 of b.69, where the r.h. grace-notes should coincide with the l.h. chord, and be followed as quickly as possibly by the top E flat. A very big *rit.* is needed in b.71 to disperse the climax and arrive smoothly at the *Più Adagio*, which is considerably slower than the rest of the movement. Note that the pedal-change in bb.73, 75, etc., is on the 2nd quaver, *not* on the note before. The six r.h. semiquavers beginning in bb.73 & 75 could be on a lower dynamic level than the rest, as though heard from afar.

3 INTERMEZZO IN C SHARP MINOR

Andante con moto [♪ = c.84];
Poco più lento [♪ = c.76];
Più moto [♩ = c.66];
Più lento [♪ = c.69]

Some players may find the following layout more comfortable:

If so, it can also be used for the r.h. in bb.6-9, while the l.h. omits the 4th & 8th semiquaver in each bar. Whichever version is used, it is important not to lose the slurring of the paired semiquavers within the longer phrases. In bb.19-20 the octave melody between the lowest line in each hand ends with the octave C sharp in b.20, as can be seen from bb.40 & 104: the descending quaver 6ths are subsidiary. On the other hand, in bb.25 & 30 the melody is concluded by, respectively, the lowest and the middle r.h. line.

In the *Più moto* the pedal-changes in bb.46-48, etc., are on the 4th and 8th semiquaver. As soon as the l.h. has played beat 1 in each bar, let it move *above* the r.h., into precisely the right position for playing the first of its four semiquavers. (This avoids collisions between the two hands.) Bb.59-60 become less confusing if the r.h. thumb leads throughout and care is taken to keep close to the keys while reaching for the G sharp and D sharp. A fraction of extra time in b.72 will ensure that the l.h. G natural (instead of the expected D sharp as in b.52) comes as a surprise.

Note in bb.80 & 83 that the pauses are marked *between* the chords and are therefore silent, like the one in b.20 of the Intermezzo in E flat (see p.9).

The final *Più lento* (b.105) is slower than the *Poco più lento* of b.40, as though to underline the sombre mood of the whole.

THREE INTERMEZZOS
Op. 117

BRAHMS

Balow, my babe, lie still and sleep!
It grieves me sore to see thee weep.
(Scottish: 'Lady Anne Bothwell's Lament')

Schlaf sanft, mein Kind, schlaf sanft und schön!
Mich dauert's sehr dich weinen sehn.
(Schottisch: aus Herder's Volksliedern)

(a) Arpeggio begins on the beat.   (b) R.h. chord coincides with the top note of the l.h. arpeggio.

AB 1959

Più adagio

Un poco più andante

(c) The r.h. chord coincides with the top note of the l.h. arpeggio.

Andante non troppo e con molto espressione

(a) Arpeggios begin on the beat.

(b) Gracenotes *on* the beat.

Andante con moto

3

*(a) molto **p** e sotto voce sempre*

p legato

(a) For an alternative fingering see the Editorial Notes, p. 7.
1) B. 15: in the source the upper slur ends on the A sharp; but see the more probable b. 35.

Più moto ed espressivo
dolce ma espress.